Dr. Seuss's ABC

By
Dr. Seuss

HarperCollins *Children's Books*

The Cat in the Hat
™ & © Dr. Seuss Enterprises, L.P. 1957
All Rights Reserved

A CIP catalogue record for this title is available from
the British Library.

1 3 5 7 9 10 8 6 4 2

ISBN 978-0-00-820391-7

© 1963, 1991 by Dr. Seuss Enterprises, L.P.
All Rights Reserved
Published by arrangement with
Random House Inc., New York, USA
First published in the UK 1964
This edition published in the UK 2017 by
HarperCollins *Children's Books,*
a division of HarperCollins*Publishers* Ltd
1 London Bridge Street
London SE1 9GF

Visit our website at:
www.harpercollins.co.uk

Printed and Bound in China

BIG A

little   a

What begins with A?

Aunt Annie's alligator . .

. . . . . A . . a . . A

BIG B

little   b

What begins with B?

Barber
baby
bubbles
and a
bumblebee.

BIG C

little   c

What begins with C?

Camel on the ceiling
C . . . . c C

BIG D

little   d

David Donald Doo
dreamed
a dozen doughnuts
and
a duck-dog, too.

ABCDE..e..e

ear

egg

elephant

e

e

E

BIG F

little   f

F.. f.. F

Four fluffy feathers
on a
Fiffer-feffer-feff.

ABCD
EFG

Goat
girl
googoo goggles
G . . . g . . . G

BIG H

little   h

Hungry horse.
Hay.

Hen in a hat.
Hooray !
Hooray !

BIG I

little   i

i . . . . i i

Icabod
is
itchy.

So am I.

BIG J

little   j

What begins with j?

Jerry Jordan's
jelly jar
and jam
begin that way.

BIG K

little   k

Kitten. Kangaroo.

Kick a kettle.
Kite
and a
king's kerchoo.

27

BIG L

little   l

Little Lola Lopp.
Left leg.
Lazy lion
licks a lollipop.

BIG M

little   m

Many mumbling mice
are making
midnight music
in the moonlight . . .

mighty nice

BIG N

little　　　n

What begins with those?

Nine new neckties
and a nightshirt
and a nose.

O is very useful.
You use it when you say:
"Oscar's only ostrich
oiled
an orange owl today."

ABCD EFG HIJK LMNO..

... P

Painting pink pyjamas.
Policeman in a pail.

Peter Pepper's puppy.
And now
Papa's in the pail.

BIG Q

little q

What begins with Q ?

The quick
Queen of Quincy
and her
quacking quacker-oo.

QUACK
QUACK

41

BIG R
little r
Rosy Robin Ross.

Rosy's going riding
on her
red rhinoceros.

BIG S

little s

Silly Sammy Slick
sipped six sodas
and got
sick sick sick.

T . . . . T
t . . . . . . t

What begins with T?

Ten tired turtles
on a tuttle-tuttle tree.

BIG U

little   u

What begins with U?

Uncle Ubb's umbrella
and his
underwear, too.

BIG V

little   v

Vera Violet Vinn
 is
very
very
very awful
on her violin.

W . . w . . W

Willy Waterloo
washes Warren Wiggins
who is
washing Waldo Woo.

X is very useful
if your name is
Nixie Knox.
It also
comes in handy
spelling axe
and extra fox.

NIXIE KNOX

BIG Y

little   y

A yawning yellow yak.
Young Yolanda Yorgenson
is yelling on his back.

BIG Z

little   z

What begins with Z?

I do.

I am a
Zizzer-Zazzer-Zuzz
as you can
plainly see.

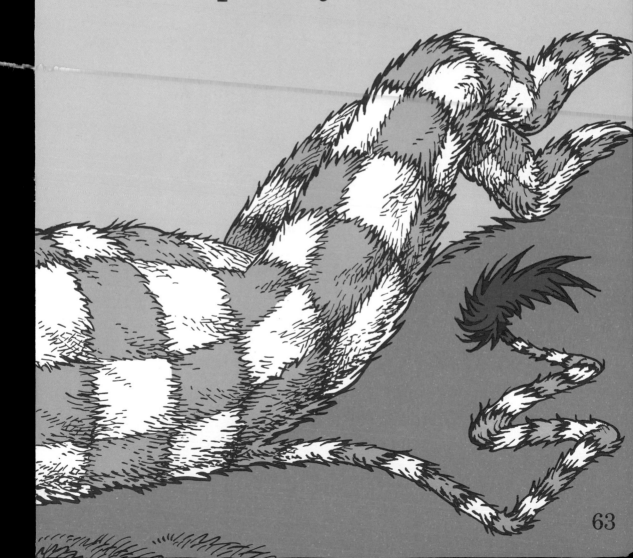